P9-AOR-637

MTV's BEAVIS AND BUTT-HEAD

DOODXiE BOOK#2

HUH HUH.
NUMBER TWO.

BEAVIS AND BUTT-HEAD CREATED BY MIKE JUDGE

COMPILED BY:
DOMINIE MAHL
KRISTOFOR BROWN
SARA DUFFY
BRAD MACDONALD
JAMES D WOOD

SPECIAL THANKS TO CHRISTINE BROWN

"HOW TO DRAW US" PAGE TAKEN FROM "THIS BOOK SUCKS" BY SAM JOHNSON AND CHRIS MARCIL

©1997 MTV NETWORKS. ALL RIGHTS RESERVED. "MTV MUSIC TELEVISION", "BEAVIS AND BUTT-HEAD" AND ALL RELATED LOGOS, TITLES AND CHARACTERS ARE TRADEMARKS OF MTV NETWORKS, A DIVISION OF VIACOM INTERNATIONAL INC."

PUBLISHED BY BOSTON AMERICA CORP., 125 WALNUT STREET, WATERTOWN, MA 02172
LAYOUT BY COFFEYCUP PRODUCTIONS.

DO THE BUTT-HEAD

FIGURE 1: MOVE HIPS BACK AND FORTH VIGOROUSLY. KEEP YOUR FEET IN PLACE.

HIP MOVEMENT

FIGURE 2: STOP HIP ACTION AND MAKE A SLAPPING MOTION WHILE THE FEET REMAIN IN PLACE

SLAPPING MOTION

DO THE BEAVIS

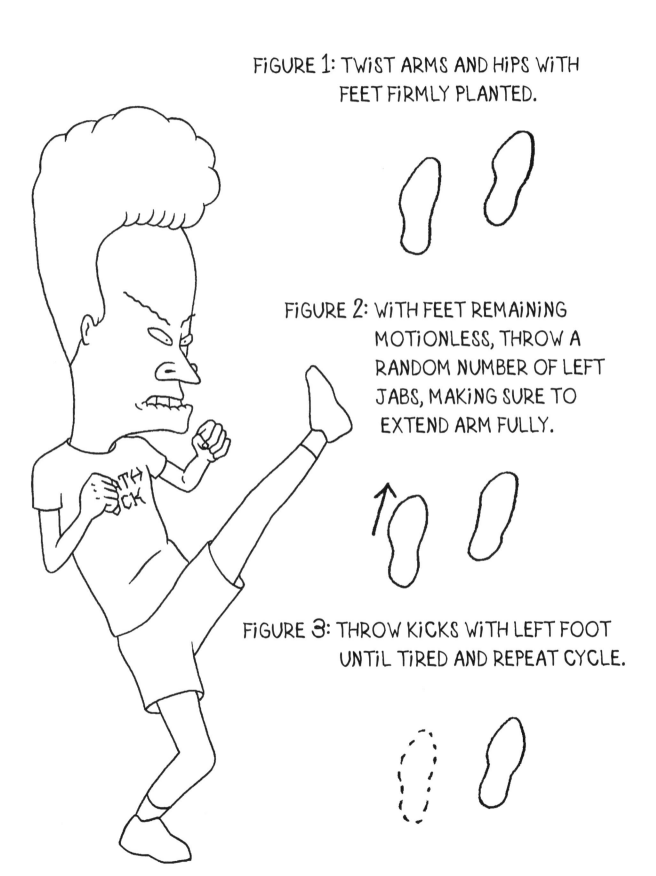

FIGURE 1: TWIST ARMS AND HIPS WITH FEET FIRMLY PLANTED.

FIGURE 2: WITH FEET REMAINING MOTIONLESS, THROW A RANDOM NUMBER OF LEFT JABS, MAKING SURE TO EXTEND ARM FULLY.

FIGURE 3: THROW KICKS WITH LEFT FOOT UNTIL TIRED AND REPEAT CYCLE.

LET'S DRAW NAKED CHICKS

PUPPET SHOW

Like, this is a script for like, a really cool puppet show, starring me and Beavis. You should like, get all your neighbors to come over and watch, and then like, charge them five bucks.
Then you're s'posed to send me all of the money for using my play. It's called royalty or something. I guess if you write a play, it's like, you become a king or queen or something, and everyone has to send you money. Huh huh. Royalty rules.
So anyways, uh, here's the play:

"A Time To Score" by Butt-Head
(Direction: Uhh, like, I guess you should have the puppets standing next to each other for this play.)

BUTT-HEAD: Hey. How's it goin'?

BEAVIS: Um, pretty good.

BUTT-HEAD: Hey Beavis, wanna go pick up some chicks?

BEAVIS: Yeah. That'd be cool.

BUTT-HEAD: Yeah, really.
(Direction: Have the puppets walk away for like, a half hour. And then have them come back.)

BUTT-HEAD: Whoa. That was cool.

BEAVIS: Yeah, really.

BUTT-HEAD: Those chicks were sluts. Huh huh.

THE END

Cut out along dotted lines and tape ice cream pop stick to the back.

CONNECT
THE DOTS

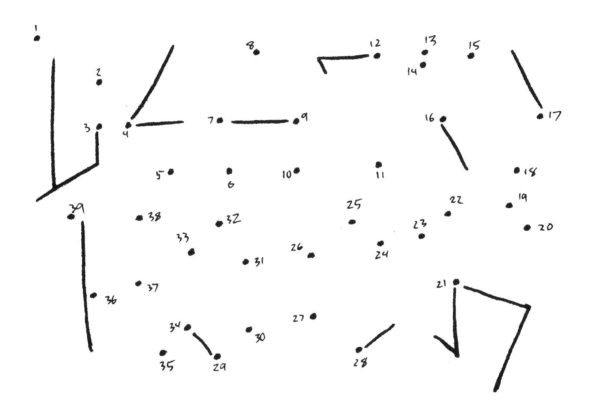

CONNECT THE DOTS

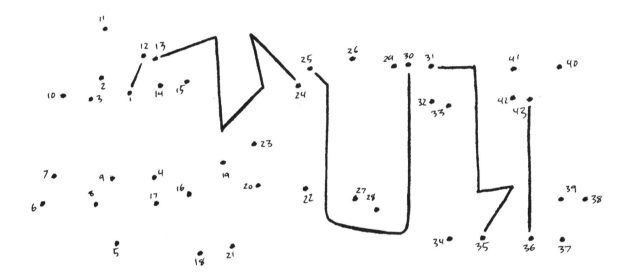

DRAW YOUR OWN ROCK BAND

HOW TO DRAW US

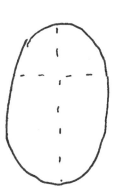

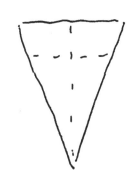

LET'S SAY YOU'RE LIKE BORED, AND
YOU WANNA DRAW ME AND BEAVIS.
THAT WOULD BE COOL.
SHUT UP, BEAVIS. OKAY, FIRST YOU
START WITH THE HEAD.
HEH HEH M HEH HEH. YOU SAID HEAD.
HUH HUH. COOL. OKAY FOR BEAVIS,
DRAW LIKE A TRIANGLE WITH LIKE ONE
POINT GOING STRAIGHT DOWN.
THAT'S HIS HEAD. HUH HUH HUH. OH
YEAH, DRAW LIKE A CROSS IN IT.
THAT'S FOR, UH, BECAUSE, UH, JUST
DO IT AND DON'T ASK ANY QUESTIONS.
HEH HEH. BUTT-HEAD'S HEAD IS
LIKE A VOLVO.
OVAL, DUMB ASS.
HEH HEH. YEAH, OVAL. UH, PUT A
CROSS IN IT.
FOR BEAVIS'S FACE? FIRST DO HIS
HAIR. HUH HUH, IT'S LIKE MESSED UP.
BUTT-HEAD'S EYE'S ARE LITTLE. HEH
HEH. LIKE LITTLE BURNED UP SEEDS.
UH, MAKE BEAVIS'S TEETH MESSED UP.
BUTT-HEAD'S GOT LIKE BIG GUMS. HEH
HEH. LIKE PIECES OF RAW CHICKEN.
PUT EGGS AND CRAP ON HIS BRACES.
HE LIKES TO MUNCH.
UH, BEAVIS'S NOSE IS SORT OF LIKE,
UH, MESSED UP.
BUTT-HEAD'S NOSTRILS ARE BIG.
THEY'RE LIKE ANIMAL CAVERS THAT GO
IN HIS FACE. HEH HEH.
WHEN YOU'RE DONE,
THROW IT ANY.

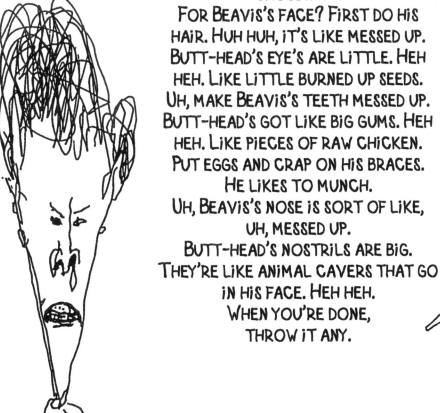

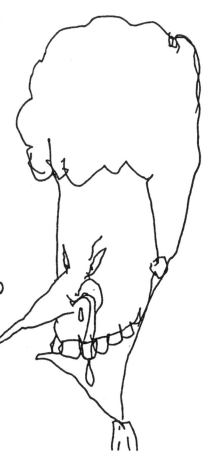

FILL IN THE ACTION

CAN YOU FIND BEAVIS?

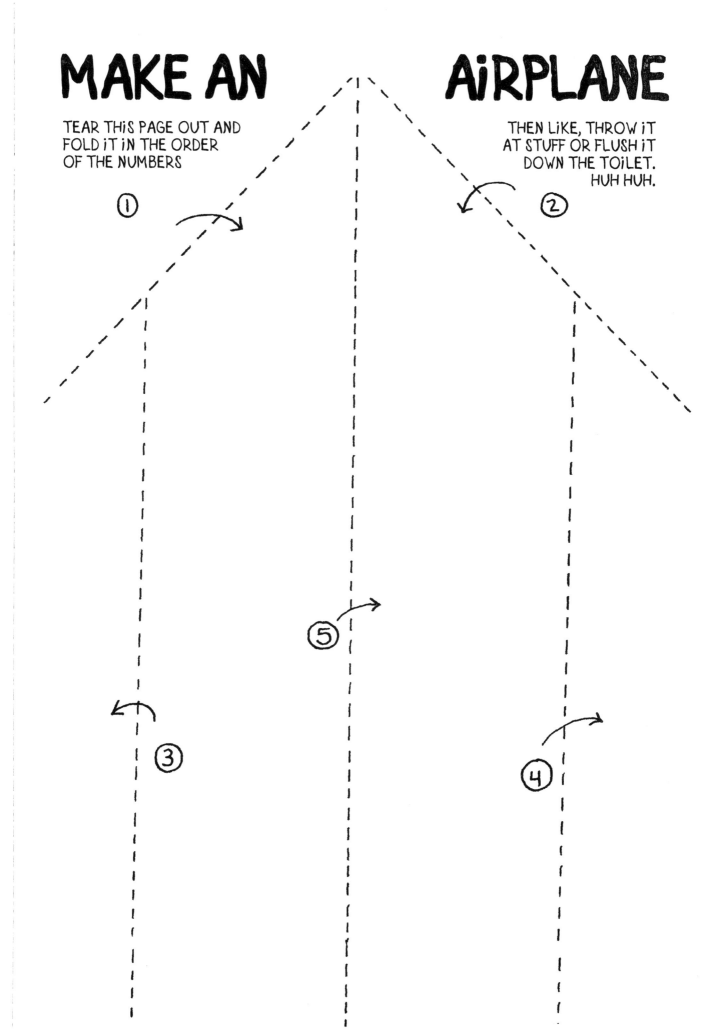

DANCING FINGER DUDES

CUT OUT ALONG DOTTED LINES. THEN STICK YOUR FINGERS THROUGH THE LEG HOLES AND PRACTICE YOUR DANCE MOVES

EMERGENCY T.P.

CUT ALONG DOTTED LINES, CRUMPLE AND WIPE.

NACHO MAZE

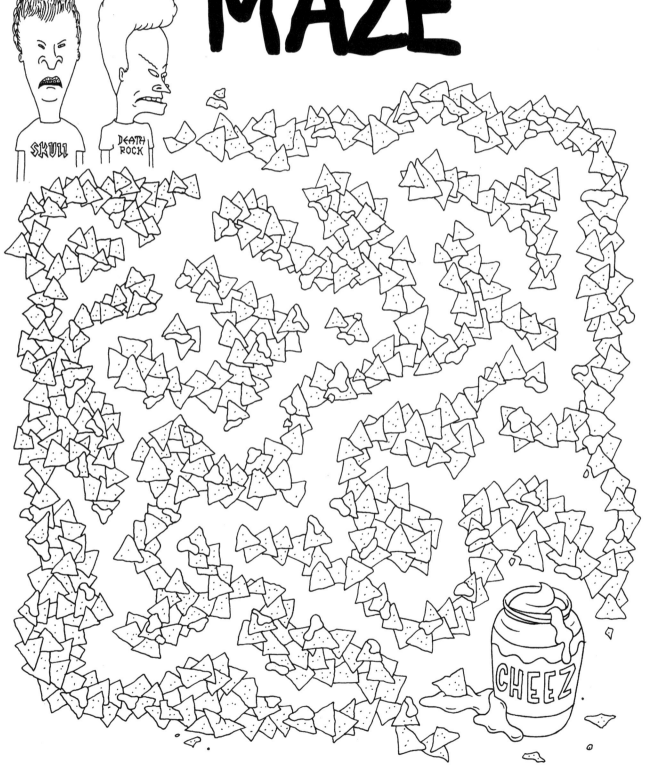

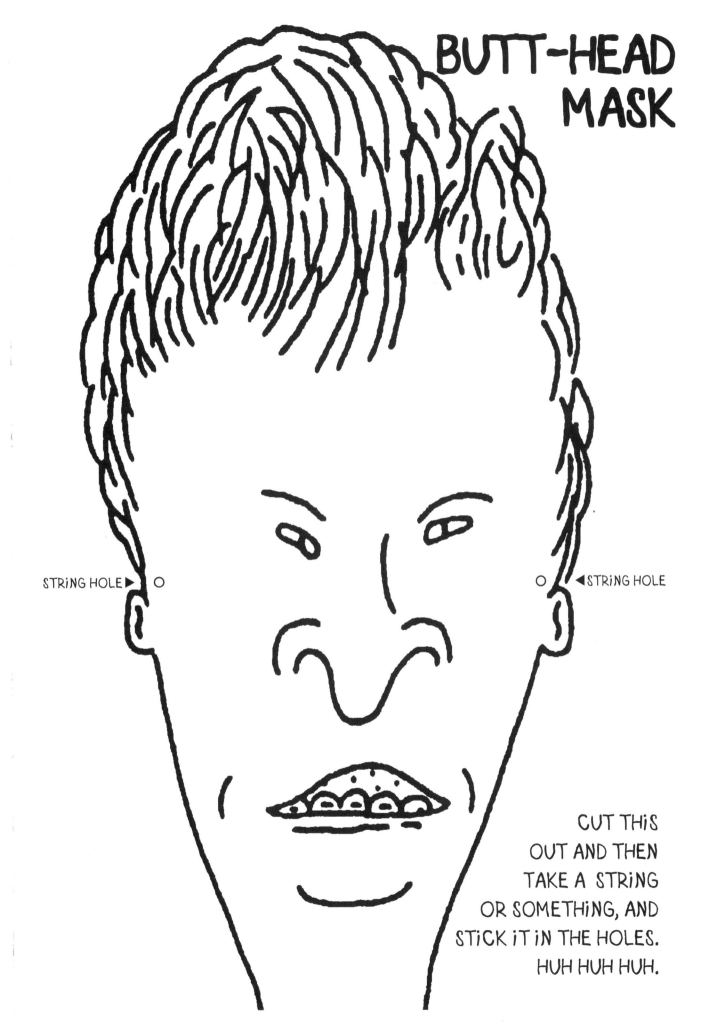

BUTT-HEAD MASK

STRING HOLE ▶ O

O ◀ STRING HOLE

CUT THIS
OUT AND THEN
TAKE A STRING
OR SOMETHING, AND
STICK IT IN THE HOLES.
HUH HUH HUH.

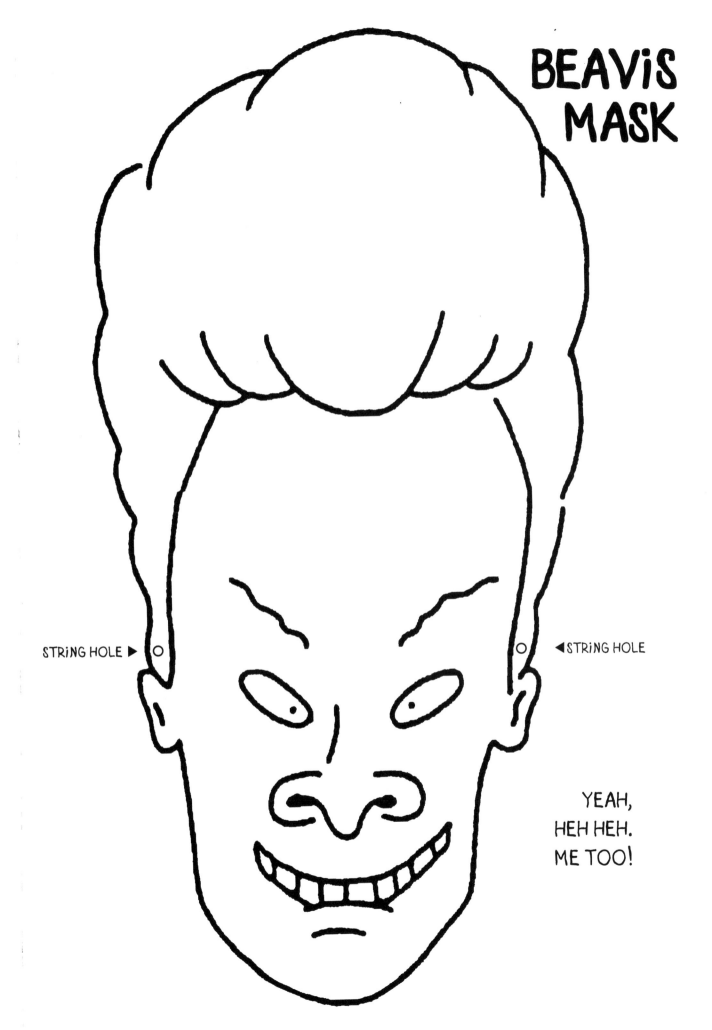

BEAViS
MASK

STRING HOLE ▶ ○

○ ◀ STRING HOLE

YEAH,
HEH HEH.
ME TOO!

PAPER DOLLS

FOLD ALONG DOTTED LINES
CUT ALONG SOLID LINES

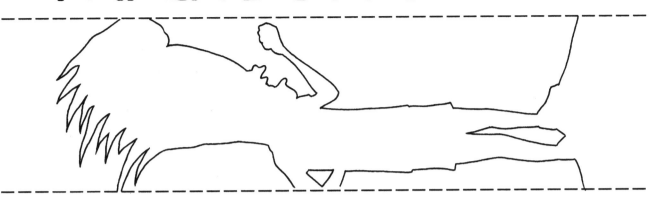

PAPER DOLLS FOLD ALONG DOTTED LINES

PAPER DOLLS

FOLD ALONG DOTTED LINES
CUT ALONG SOLID LINES

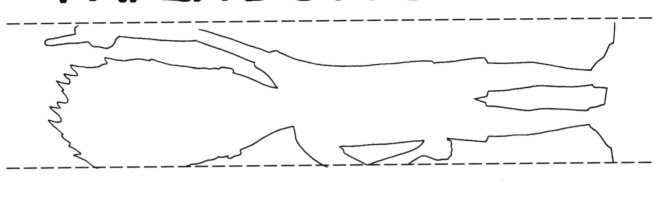

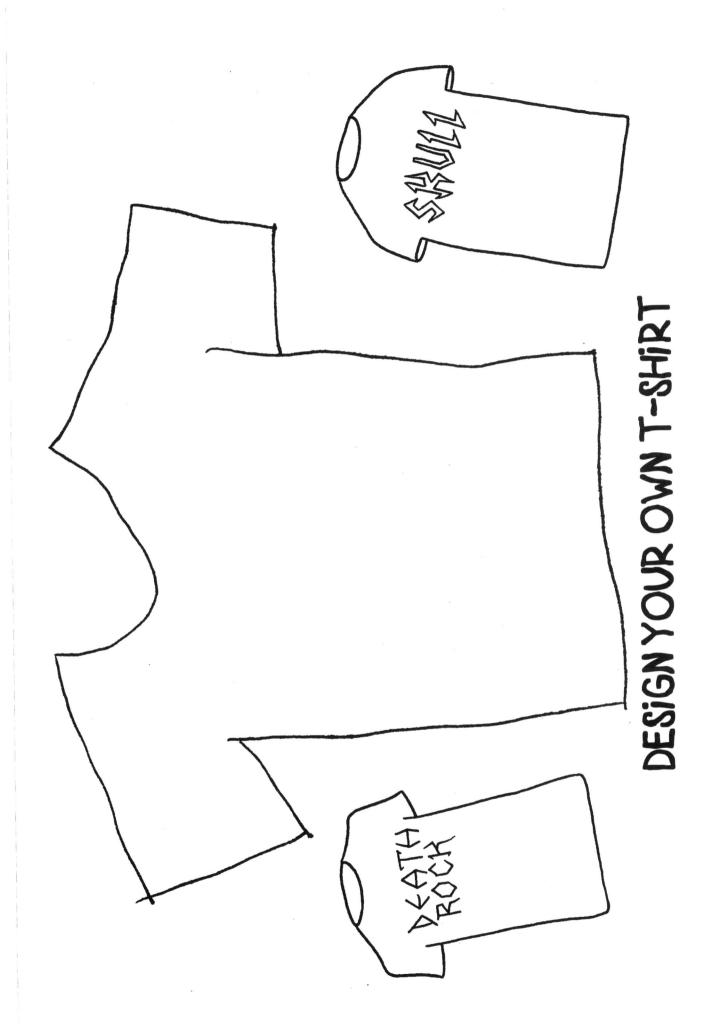

DESIGN YOUR OWN T-SHIRT

PROGRESS REPORT

Highland High School
Progress Report

Pupil's name: *Beavis*

Grade: *10*

Attendence	
Days absent:	14
Classes tardy:	47
Mathematics:	F
History:	F
Science:	F
English:	F
Physical Education:	N
Elective courses:	
Wood shop	F
Listens to and follows directions:	U
Completes work on time:	F
Participates in class discussions:	N
Is courteous:	N
Interacts well with others:	N
Maintains positive attitude and outlook:	U
Respects school property:	F

EXPLANATION OF MARKS

S- Satisfactory   U- Unsatisfactory
N- Needs improvement   I- Improvement shown
F- Failing

COMMENTS: *I'm very concerned about Beavis. He actually seems to be 'losing intelligence.'*
—David Van Driessen

Please return with parent's signature
Parent's signature: _____

Check it out, Beavis is a dumbass. Huh huh huh.

CONNECT THE DOTS

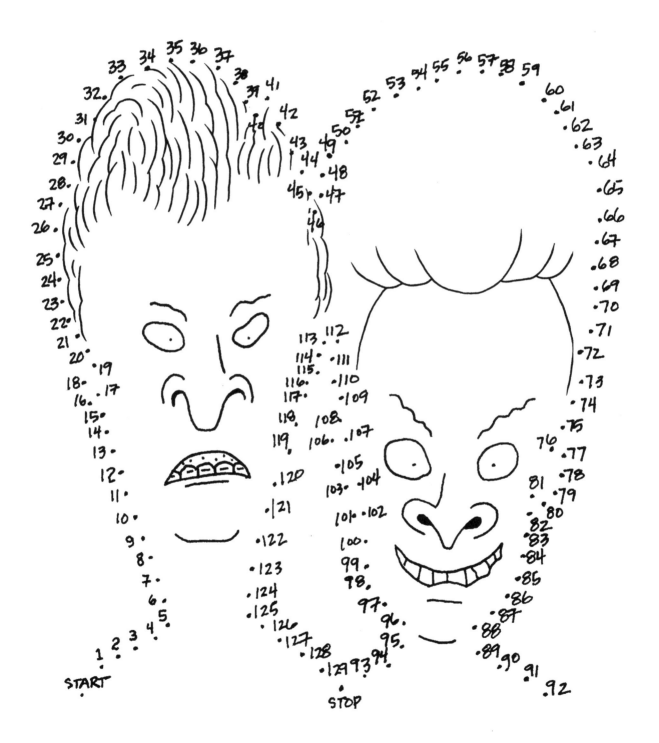

START

STOP

MAKE YOUR OWN NACHOS

CUT OUT AND COLOR. NACHOS: LIGHT BROWN
CHEESE: CHEESE COLOR, DUMBASS.

NACHOS RULE!

MAKE YOUR OWN NACHO BOAT

CUT OUT AND COLOR EVERY OTHER STRIPE RED

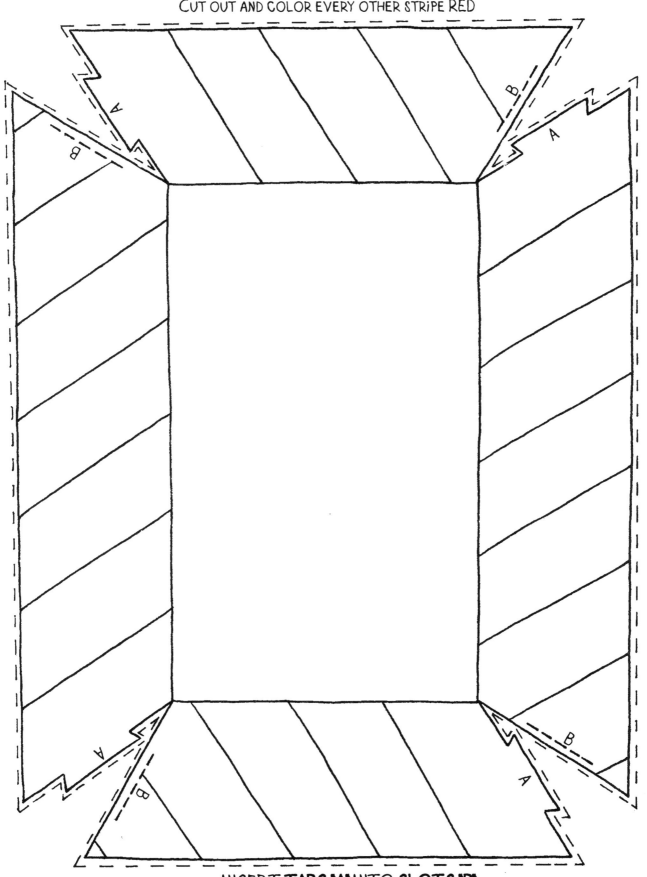

INSERT TABS "A" INTO SLOTS "B"

MEMORY TEST

UH, LOOK AT THIS PICTURE FOR, LIKE, AN HOUR AR SOMETHING AND
TRY TO REMEMBER ALL THE STUFF YOU SEE. HUH HUH...MEMBER.
THEN LIKE, TURN THE PAGE.

MEMORY TEST

NOW, I THINK YOU'RE S'POSED TO, UH, WRITE DOWN ALL THE STUFF ON THE PAGE YOU WERE JUST LOOKING AT, OR SOMETHING. IF YOU CAN'T REMEMBER ANYTHING, JUST FLIP BACK AND LOOK AGAIN. HUH HUH HUH.

_____   _____

_____   _____

_____   _____

_____   _____

_____

_____

_____

_____

_____

_____

DAILY PLANNER

UM, HEY, HOW'S IT GOIN'? HEH HEH. THIS THING IS CALLED A DAILY PLANNER, OR SOMETHING. A LOT OF PEOPLE NEED THESE, CUZ THEY'RE LIKE, STUPID. THEY, LIKE, CAN'T REMEMBER TO DO IMPORTANT THINGS LIKE, WATCHING T.V. AND LIKE, UM... UM... WATCHING T.V. AND STUFF.

SO, LIKE, HERE'S ONE OF THESE DAILY PLANNER PAGES THAT YOU CAN USE. I, LIKE, PUT SOME STUFF IN TO GET YOU STARTED.

Sunday	Watch T.V. Eat Nachos.
Monday	Go to school. Watch t.v.
Tuesday	Go to school. Watch t.v. poop.
Wednesday	Skip school to watch t.v. eat nachos
Thursday	poop. Go to school. stay up all night watching t.v.
Friday	too tired to go to school. watch t.v.
Saturday	eat nachos. 'Baywatch' Spank monkey

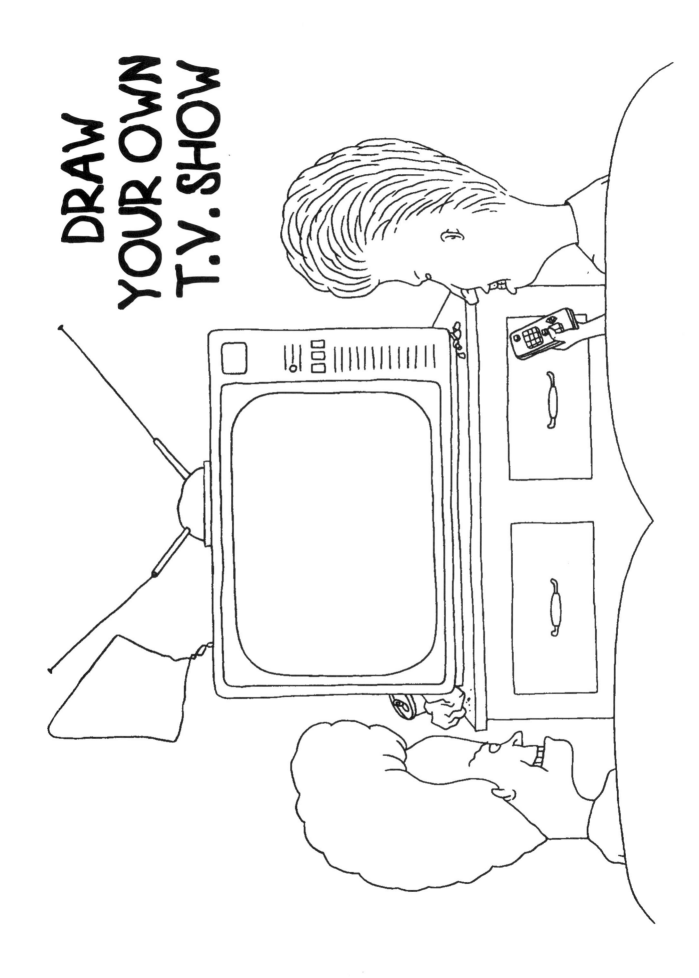

DRAW
YOUR OWN
T.V. SHOW

ANIMATE BEAVIS AND BUTT-HEAD

ANIMATION IS WHEN YOU, LIKE, DRAW A BUNCH OF PICTURES ONE ON TOP OF THE OTHER....

HEH HEH. ON TOP. HEH HEH.

SHUT UP, DILLWEED, I'M LIKE, TRYING TO SAY STUFF. UH, WHERE WAS I? OH YEAH. AFTER YOU HAVE, LIKE, A BUNCH OF DRAWINGS 'N STUFF, YOU UH, FLIP 'EM OR SOMETHING AND THEN YOU'RE SUPPOSED TO SEE A CARTOON. IT'S PRETTY COOL, BUT YOU HAVE TO HAVE A LOT OF DRAWINGS. SO, LIKE, IF EVERYTHING ON TV SUCKS OR YOUR TV'S BROKEN, YOU COULD TRACE THIS PICTURE OF ME AND BEAVIS, LIKE, A MILLION TIMES OR SOMETHING, AND THEN WATCH US STAND THERE. HUH HUH HUH.